THE NEWCASTLE FORGOTTEN FANTASY LIBRARY
VOLUME III

THE FOOD OF DEATH
FIFTY-ONE TALES

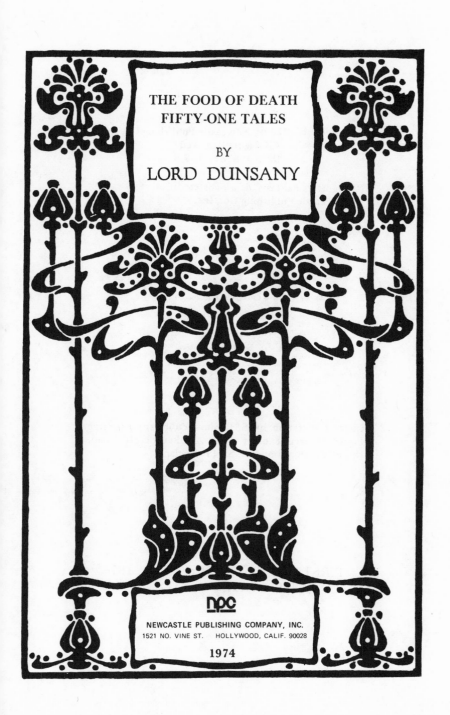

THE FOOD OF DEATH
FIFTY-ONE TALES

BY

LORD DUNSANY

NEWCASTLE PUBLISHING COMPANY, INC.
1521 NO. VINE ST.   HOLLYWOOD, CALIF. 90028

1974

Library of Congress Cataloging in Publication Data

Dunsany, Edward John Moreton Drax Plunkett, Baron,
    1878-1957.
    The food of death: fifty-one tales.

    (Newcastle Forgotten Fantasy classic F-102)
    Reprint of the 1915-ed. published by M. Kennerley,
New York, under title: Fifty-one tales.
    1. Fantastic fiction, English. I. Title.
PZ3.D9248Fm3 [PR6007.U6]   823'.9'12   74-6394
ISBN 0-87877-102-6

Cover Illustration by S.H. Sime, courtesy of George
Locke, Ferret Fantasy Ltd., 27 Beechcroft Road,
Upper Tooting, London, SW17, England

A NEWCASTLE BOOK
FIRST PRINTING: SEPTEMBER, 1974
PRINTED IN THE UNITED STATES OF AMERICA

CONTENTS

	PAGE
THE ASSIGNATION	9
CHARON	11
THE DEATH OF PAN	14
THE SPHINX AT GIZEH	16
THE HEN	19
WIND AND FOG	22
THE RAFT-BUILDERS	24
THE WORKMAN	26
THE GUEST	28
DEATH AND ODYSSEUS	32
DEATH AND THE ORANGE	34
THE PRAYER OF THE FLOWERS	36
TIME AND THE TRADESMAN	38
THE LITTLE CITY	39
THE UNPASTURABLE FIELDS	41
THE WORM AND THE ANGEL	43
THE SONGLESS COUNTRY	45
THE LATEST THING	47

CONTENTS

PAGE

THE DEMAGOGUE AND THE DEMI-MONDE 49

THE GIANT POPPY 51

ROSES 53

THE MAN WITH THE GOLDEN EAR-RINGS 55

THE DREAM OF KING KARNA-VOOTRA 58

THE STORM 62

A MISTAKEN IDENTITY 65

TRUE HISTORY OF THE HARE AND THE TORTOISE 66

ALONE THE IMMORTALS 71

A MORAL LITTLE TALE 75

THE RETURN OF SONG 79

SPRING IN TOWN 81

HOW THE ENEMY CAME TO THLUMANA 85

A LOSING GAME 89

TAKING UP PICCADILLY 91

AFTER THE FIRE 93

THE CITY 94

THE FOOD OF DEATH 96

THE LONELY IDOL 97

THE SPHINX IN THEBES (MASSACHUSETTS) 100

THE REWARD 102

THE TROUBLE IN LEAFY GREEN STREET 105

THE MIST 107

FURROW-MAKER 108

CONTENTS

	PAGE
LOBSTER SALAD	112
THE RETURN OF THE EXILES	116
NATURE AND TIME	120
THE SONG OF THE BLACKBIRD	123
THE MESSENGERS	126
THE THREE TALL SONS	132
COMPROMISE	134
WHAT WE HAVE COME TO	136
THE TOMB OF PAN	137

THE ASSIGNATION

FAME singing in the highways, and trifling as she sang, with sordid adventurers, passed the poet by.

And still the poet made for her little chaplets of song, to deck her forehead in the courts of Time: and still she wore instead the worthless garlands, that boisterous citizens flung to her in the ways, made out of perishable things.

And after a while whenever these garlands died the poet came to her with his chaplets of song; and still she laughed at him and wore the worthless wreaths, though they always died at evening.

And one day in his bitterness the poet rebuked her, and said to her: "Lovely Fame, even in the highways and the byways you have not forborne to laugh and shout

9

and jest with worthless men, and I have toiled for you and dreamed of you and you mock me and pass me by."

And Fame turned her back on him and walked away, but in departing she looked over her shoulder and smiled at him as she had not smiled before, and, almost speaking in a whisper, said:

"I will meet you in the graveyard at the back of the Workhouse in a hundred years."

CHARON

CHARON leaned forward and rowed. All things were one with his weariness.

It was not with him a matter of years or of centuries, but of wide floods of time, and an old heaviness and a pain in the arms that had become for him part of the scheme that the gods had made and was of a piece with Eternity.

If the gods had even sent him a contrary wind it would have divided all time in his memory into two equal slabs.

So grey were all things always where he was that if any radiance lingered a moment among the dead, on the face of such a queen perhaps as Cleopatra, his eyes could not have perceived it.

It was strange that the dead nowadays

were coming in such numbers. They were coming in thousands where they used to come in fifties. It was neither Charon's duty nor his wont to ponder in his grey soul why these things might be. Charon leaned forward and rowed.

Then no one came for a while. It was not usual for the gods to send no one down from Earth for such a space. But the gods knew best.

Then one man came alone. And the little shade sat shivering on a lonely bench and the great boat pushed off. Only one passenger; the gods knew best. And great and weary Charon rowed on and on beside the little, silent, shivering ghost.

And the sound of the river was like a mighty sigh that Grief in the beginning had sighed among her sisters, and that could not die like the echoes of human sorrow failing on earthly hills, but was as old as time and the pain in Charon's arms.

Then the boat from the slow, grey river

loomed up to the coast of Dis and the little, silent shade still shivering stepped ashore, and Charon turned the boat to go wearily back to the world. Then the little shadow spoke, that had been a man.

"I am the last," he said.

No one had ever made Charon smile before, no one before had ever made him weep.

THE DEATH OF PAN

WHEN the travellers from London entered Arcady they lamented one to another the death of Pan.

And anon they saw him lying stiff and still.

Horned Pan was still and the dew was on his fur; he had not the look of a live animal. And then they said: "It is true that Pan is dead."

And, standing melancholy by that huge prone body, they looked for long at memorable Pan.

And evening came and a small star appeared.

And presently from a hamlet of some Arcadian valley, with a sound of idle song, Arcadian maidens came.

And, when they saw there, suddenly in

14

the twilight, that old recumbent god, they stopped in their running and whispered among themselves. " How silly he looks," they said, and thereat they laughed a little.

And at the sound of their laughter Pan leaped up and the gravel flew from his hooves.

And, for as long as the travellers stood and listened, the crags and the hill-tops of Arcady rang with the sounds of pursuit.

THE SPHINX AT GIZEH

I SAW the other day the Sphinx's painted face.

She had painted her face in order to ogle Time.

And he has spared no other painted face in all the world but hers.

Delilah was younger than she, and Delilah is dust.

Time hath loved nothing but this worthless painted face.

I do not care that she is ugly, nor that she has painted her face, so that she only lure his secret from Time.

Time dallies like a fool at her feet when he should be smiting cities.

Time never wearies of her silly smile.

There are temples all about her that he has forgotten to spoil.

16

I saw an old man go by, and Time never touched him.

Time that has carried away the seven gates of Thebes!

She has tried to bind him with ropes of eternal sand, she had hoped to oppress him with the Pyramids.

He lies there in the sand with his foolish hair all spread about her paws.

If she ever finds his secret we will put out his eyes, so that he shall find no more our beautiful things—there are lovely gates in Florence that I fear he will carry away.

We have tried to bind him with song and with old customs, but they only held him for a little while, and he has always smitten us and mocked us.

When he is blind he shall dance to us and make sport.

Great clumsy Time shall stumble and dance, who liked to kill little children, and can hurt even the daisies no longer.

Then shall our children laugh at him who

slew Babylon's winged bulls, and smote great numbers of the gods and fairies— when he is shorn of his hours and his years.

We will shut him up in the Pyramid of Cheops, in the great chamber where the sarcophagus is. Thence we will lead him out when we give our feasts. He shall ripen our corn for us and do menial work.

We will kiss thy painted face, O Sphinx, if thou wilt betray to us Time.

And yet I fear that in his ultimate anguish he may take hold blindly of the world and the moon, and slowly pull down upon him the House of Man.

THE HEN

ALL along the farmyard gables the swallows sat a-row, twittering uneasily to one another, telling of many things, but thinking only of Summer and the South, for Autumn was afoot and the North wind waiting.

And suddenly one day they were all quite gone. And everyone spoke of the swallows and the South.

"I think I shall go South myself next year," said a hen.

And the year wore on and the swallows came again, and the year wore on and they sat again on the gables, and all the poultry discussed the departure of the hen.

And very early one morning, the wind being from the North, the swallows all soared suddenly and felt the wind in their wings; and a strength came upon them and a strange old knowledge and a more than human faith, and flying high they left the smoke of our cities and small remembered eaves, and saw at last the huge and home-less sea, and steering by grey sea-currents went southward with the wind. And going South they went by glittering fog-banks and saw old islands lifting their heads above them; they saw the slow quests of the wandering ships, and divers seeking pearls, and lands at war, till there came in view the mountains that they sought and the sight of the peaks they knew; and they descended into an austral valley, and saw Summer sometimes sleeping and sometimes singing song.

"I think the wind is about right," said the hen; and she spread her wings and ran out of the poultry-yard. And she ran flut-tering out on to the road and some way down it until she came to a garden.

At evening she came back panting.

And in the poultry-yard she told the poultry how she had gone South as far as the high road, and saw the great world's traffic going by, and came to lands where the potato grew, and saw the stubble upon which men live, and at the end of the road had found a garden, and there were roses in it—beautiful roses!—and the gardener himself was there with his braces on.

"How extremely interesting," the poultry said, "and what a really beautiful description!"

And the Winter wore away, and the bitter months went by, and the Spring of the year appeared, and the swallows came again.

"We have been to the South," they said, "and the valleys beyond the sea."

But the poultry would not agree that there was a sea in the South: "You should hear our hen," they said.

WIND AND FOG

W AY for us," said the North Wind as he came down the sea on an errand of old Winter.

And he saw before him the grey silent fog that lay along the tides.

"Way for us," said the North Wind, "O ineffectual fog, for I am Winter's leader in his age-old war with the ships. I overwhelm them suddenly in my strength, or drive upon them the huge seafaring bergs. I cross an ocean while you move a mile. There is mourning in inland places when I have met the ships. I drive them upon the rocks and feed the sea. Wherever I appear they bow to our lord the Winter."

And to his arrogant boasting nothing said the fog. Only he rose up slowly and trailed away from the sea and, crawling up long valleys, took refuge among the hills; and night came down and everything was still, and the fog began to mumble in the stillness. And I heard him telling infamously to himself the tale of his horrible spoils. "A hundred and fifteen galleons of old Spain, a certain argosy that went from Tyre, eight fisher-fleets and ninety ships of the line, twelve warships under sail, with their carronades, three hundred and eighty-seven river-craft, forty-two merchantmen that carried spice, four quinquiremes, ten triremes, thirty yachts, twenty-one battle-ships of the modern time, nine thousand admirals . . ." he mumbled and chuckled on, till I suddenly rose and fled from his fearful contamination.

THE RAFT-BUILDERS

ALL we who write put me in mind of sailors hastily making rafts upon doomed ships.

When we break up under the heavy years and go down into eternity with all that is ours our thoughts like small lost rafts float on awhile upon Oblivion's sea. They will not carry much over those tides, our names and a phrase or two and little else.

They that write as a trade to please the whim of the day, they are like sailors that work at the rafts only to warm their hands and to distract their thoughts from their certain doom; their rafts go all to pieces before the ship breaks up.

See now Oblivion shimmering all around us, its very tranquillity deadlier than tempest. How little all our keels have troubled it. Time in its deeps swims like a monstrous whale; and, like a whale, feeds on the littlest things—small tunes and little unskilled songs of the olden, golden evenings—and anon turneth whale-like to overthrow whole ships.

See now the wreckage of Babylon floating idly, and something there that once was Nineveh; already their kings and queens are in the deeps among the weedy masses of old centuries that hide the sodden hulk of sunken Tyre and make a darkness round Persepolis.

For the rest I dimly see the forms of foundered ships on the sea-floor strewn with crowns.

Our ships were all unseaworthy from the first.

There goes the raft that Homer made for Helen.

THE WORKMAN

I SAW a workman fall with his scaffolding right from the summit of some vast hotel. And as he came down I saw him holding a knife and trying to cut his name on the scaffolding. He had time to try and do this for he must have had nearly three hundred feet to fall. And I could think of nothing but his folly in doing this futile thing, for not only would the man be unrecognizably dead in three seconds, but the very pole on which he tried to scratch whatever of his name he had time for was certain to be burnt in a few weeks for firewood.

Then I went home for I had work to do. And all that evening I thought of the man's folly, till the thought hindered me from serious work.

And late that night while I was still at work, the ghost of the workman floated through my wall and stood before me laughing.

I heard no sound until after I spoke to it; but I could see the grey diaphanous form standing before me shuddering with laughter.

I spoke at last and asked what it was laughing at, and then the ghost spoke. It said: "I'm a-laughin' at you sittin' and workin' there."

"And why," I said, "do you laugh at serious work?"

"Why, yer bloomin' life 'ull go by like a wind," he said, "and yer 'ole silly civilization 'ull be tidied up in a few centuries."

Then he fell to laughing again and this time audibly; and, laughing still, faded back through the wall again and into the eternity from which he had come.

THE GUEST

A YOUNG man came into an ornate restaurant at eight o'clock in London.

He was alone, but two places had been laid at the table which was reserved for him. He had chosen the dinner very carefully, by letter a week before.

A waiter asked him about the other guest.

"You probably won't see him till the coffee comes," the young man told him; so he was served alone.

Those at adjacent tables might have noticed the young man continually addressing the empty chair and carrying on a monologue with it throughout his elaborate dinner.

"I think you knew my father," he said to it over the soup.

"I sent for you this evening," he contin-

28

ued, "because I want you to do me a good
turn; in fact I must insist on it."

There was nothing eccentric about the
man except for this habit of addressing an
empty chair, certainly he was eating as good
a dinner as any sane man could wish for.

After the Burgundy had been served he
became more voluble in his monologue, not
that he spoiled his wine by drinking exces-
sively.

"We have several acquaintances in com-
mon," he said. "I met King Seti a year
ago in Thebes. I should think he has altered
very little since you knew him. I thought
his forehead a little low for a king's.
Cheops has left the house that he built for
your reception, he must have prepared for
you for years and years. I suppose you have
seldom been entertained like that. I ordered
this dinner over a week ago. I thought then
that a lady might have come with me, but as
she wouldn't I've asked you. She may not
after all be as lovely as Helen of Troy. Was

Helen very lovely? Not when you knew her, perhaps. You were lucky in Cleopatra, you must have known her when she was in her prime.

"You never knew the mermaids nor the fairies nor the lovely goddesses of long ago, that's where we have the best of you."

He was silent when the waiters came to his table, but rambled merrily on as soon as they left, still turned to the empty chair.

"You know I saw you here in London only the other day. You were on a motor bus going down Ludgate Hill. It was going much too fast. London is a good place. But I shall be glad enough to leave it. It was in London I met the lady that I was speaking about. If it hadn't been for London I probably shouldn't have met her, and if it hadn't been for London she probably wouldn't have had so much besides me to amuse her. It cuts both ways."

He paused once to order coffee, gazing earnestly at the waiter and putting a sovereign into his hand. "Don't let it be chicory," said he.

The waiter brought the coffee, and the young man dropped a tabloid of some sort into his cup.

"I don't suppose you come here very often," he went on. "Well, you probably want to be going. I haven't taken you much out of your way, there is plenty for you to do in London."

Then having drunk his coffee he fell on to the floor by a foot of the empty chair, and a doctor who was dining in the room bent over him and announced to the anxious manager the visible presence of the young man's guest.

DEATH AND ODYSSEUS

IN the Olympian courts Love laughed at
Death, because he was unsightly, and
because She couldn't help it, and because he
never did anything worth doing, and because She would.

And Death hated being laughed at, and
used to brood apart thinking only of his
wrongs and of what he could do to end this
intolerable treatment.

But one day Death appeared in the courts
with an air and They all noticed it. "What
are you up to now?" said Love. And
Death with some solemnity said to Her:
"I am going to frighten Odysseus"; and
drawing about him his grey traveller's cloak
went out through the windy door with his
jowl turned earthwards.

And he came soon to Ithaca and the hall

that Athene knew, and opened the door and saw there famous Odysseus, with his white locks bending close over the fire, trying to warm his hands.

And the wind through the open door blew bitterly on Odysseus.

And Death came up behind him, and suddenly shouted.

And Odysseus went on warming his pale hands.

Then Death came close and began to mouth at him. And after a while Odysseus turned and spoke. And "Well, old servant," he said, "have your masters been kind to you since I made you work for me round Ilion?"

And Death for some while stood mute, for he thought of the laughter of Love.

Then "Come now," said Odysseus, "lend me your shoulder," and he leaning heavily on that bony joint, they went together through the open door.

DEATH AND THE ORANGE

TWO dark young men in a foreign southern land sat at a restaurant table with one woman.

And on the woman's plate was a small orange which had an evil laughter in its heart.

And both of the men would be looking at the woman all the time, and they ate little and they drank much.

And the woman was smiling equally at each.

Then the small orange that had the laughter in its heart rolled slowly off the plate on to the floor. And the dark young men both sought for it at once, and they met suddenly beneath the table, and soon they were speaking swift words to one another, and a horror and an impotence came

34

over the Reason of each as she sat helpless at the back of the mind, and the heart of the orange laughed and the woman went on smiling; and Death, who was sitting at another table, *tête-à-tête* with an old man, rose and came over to listen to the quarrel.

THE PRAYER OF THE
FLOWERS

I T was the voice of the flowers on the West
wind, the lovable, the old, the lazy West
wind, blowing ceaselessly, blowing sleepily,
going Greecewards.

"The woods have gone away, they have
fallen and left us; men love us no longer,
we are lonely by moonlight. Great engines
rush over the beautiful fields, their ways lie
hard and terrible up and down the land.

"The cancrous cities spread over the
grass, they clatter in their lairs continually,
they glitter about us blemishing the night.

"The woods are gone, O Pan, the woods,
the woods. And thou art far, O Pan, and
far away."

I was standing by night between two
railway embankments on the edge of a Mid-

land city. On one of them I saw the trains go by, once in every two minutes, and on the other, the trains went by twice in every five.

Quite close were the glaring factories, and the sky above them wore the fearful look that it wears in dreams of fever.

The flowers were right in the stride of that advancing city, and thence I heard them sending up their cry. And then I heard, beating musically up wind, the voice of Pan reproving them from Arcady—"Be patient a little, these things are not for long."

TIME AND THE TRADESMAN

ONCE Time as he prowled the world, his hair grey not with weakness but with dust of the ruin of cities, came to a furniture shop and entered the Antique department. And there he saw a man darkening the wood of a chair with dye and beating it with chains and making imitation worm-holes in it.

And when Time saw another doing his work he stood by him awhile and looked on critically.

And at last he said: "That is not how I work," and he turned the man's hair white and bent his back and put some furrows in his little cunning face; then turned and strode away, for a mighty city that was weary and sick and too long had troubled the fields was sore in need of him.

THE LITTLE CITY

I WAS in the pre-destined 11.8 from Goraghwood to Drogheda, when I suddenly saw the city. It was a little city in a valley, and only seemed to have a little smoke, and the sun caught the smoke and turned it golden, so that it looked like an old Italian picture where angels walk in the foreground and the rest is a blaze of gold. And beyond, as one could tell by the lie of land although one could not see through the golden smoke, I knew that there lay the paths of the roving ships.

All round there lay a patchwork of small fields all over the slopes of the hills, and the snow had come upon them tentatively, but already the birds of the waste had moved to the sheltered places for every omen boded more to fall. Far away some little hills blazed like an aureate bulwark broken off by age and fallen from the earthward rampart of Paradise. And aloof and dark the mountains stared unconcernedly seawards.

And when I saw those grey and watchful mountains sitting where they sat while the cities of the civilization of Araby and Asia arose like crocuses, and like crocuses fell, I wondered for how long there would be smoke in the valley and little fields on the hills.

THE UNPASTURABLE FIELDS

THUS spake the mountains: "Behold us, even us; the old ones, the grey ones, that wear the feet of Time. Time on our rocks shall break his staff and stumble: and still we shall sit majestic, even as now, hearing the sound of the sea, our old coeval sister, who nurses the bones of her children and weeps for the things she has done.

"Far, far, we stand above all things; befriending the little cities until they grow old and leave us to go among the myths.

"We are the most imperishable mountains."

And softly the clouds foregathered from far places, and crag on crag and mountain upon mountain in the likeness of Caucasus upon Himalaya came riding past the sunlight upon the backs of storms and looked

down idly from their golden heights upon
the crests of the mountains.

"Ye pass away," said the mountains.

And the clouds answered, as I dreamed
or fancied,

"We pass away, indeed we pass away,
but upon our unpasturable fields Pegasus
prances. Here Pegasus gallops and browses
upon song which the larks bring to him
every morning from far terrestrial fields.
His hoof-beats ring upon our slopes at sun-
rise as though our fields were of silver.
And breathing the dawn-wind in dilated nos-
trils, with head tossed upwards and with
quivering wings, he stands and stares from
our tremendous heights, and snorts and sees
far-future wonderful wars rage in the
creases and the folds of the togas that cover
the knees of the gods."

THE WORM AND THE ANGEL

A S he crawled from the tombs of the fallen a worm met with an angel.

And together they looked upon the kings and kingdoms, and youths and maidens and the cities of men. They saw the old men heavy in their chairs and heard the children singing in the fields. They saw far wars and warriors and walled towns, wisdom and wickedness, and the pomp of kings, and the people of all the lands that the sunlight knew.

And the worm spake to the angel saying: "Behold my food."

"βῆ δ'ἀκέων παρὰ θῖνα πολυφλοίσβοιο θαλάσσης,"

murmured the angel, for they walked by the sea, "and can you destroy that too?"

And the worm paled in his anger to a

43

greyness ill to behold, for for three thousand years he had tried to destroy that line and still its melody was ringing in his head.

THE SONGLESS COUNTRY

THE poet came unto a great country in which there were no songs. And he lamented gently for the nation that had not any little foolish songs to sing to itself at evening.

And at last he said: "I will make for them myself some little foolish songs so that they may be merry in the lanes and happy by the fireside." And for some days he made for them aimless songs such as maidens sing on the hills in the older happier countries.

Then he went to some of that nation as they sat weary with the work of the day and said to them: "I have made you some aimless songs out of the small unreasonable legends, that are somewhat akin to the wind in the vales of my childhood; and you may care to sing them in your disconsolate evenings."

And they said to him:

"If you think we have time for that kind of nonsense nowadays you cannot know much of the progress of modern commerce."

And then the poet wept for he said: "Alas! They are damned."

THE LATEST THING

I SAW an unclean-feeder by the banks of the river of Time. He crouched by orchards numerous with apples in a happy land of flowers; colossal barns stood near which the ancients had stored with grain, and the sun was golden on serene far hills behind the level lands. But his back was to all these things. He crouched and watched the river. And whatever the river chanced to send him down the unclean-feeder clutched at greedily with his arms, wading out into the water.

Now there were in those days, and indeed still are, certain uncleanly cities upon the river of Time; and from them fearfully nameless things came floating shapelessly by. And whenever the odor of these came down the river before them the unclean-feeder plunged into the dirty water and stood far out, expectant. And if he opened his mouth one saw these things on his lips.

Indeed from the upper reaches there came down sometimes the fallen rhododendron's petal, sometimes a rose; but they were useless to the unclean-feeder, and when he saw them he growled.

A poet walked beside the river's bank; his head was lifted and his look was afar; I think he saw the sea, and the hills of Fate from which the river ran. I saw the unclean-feeder standing voracious, up to his waist in that evil-smelling river.

"Look," I said to the poet.

"The current will sweep him away," the poet said.

"But those cities that poison the river," I said to him.

He answered: "Whenever the centuries melt on the hills of Fate the river terribly floods."

THE DEMAGOGUE AND THE
DEMI-MONDE

A DEMAGOGUE and a demi-mondaine chanced to arrive together at the gate of Paradise. And the Saint looked sorrowfully at them both.

"Why were you a demagogue?" he said to the first.

"Because," said the demagogue, "I stood for those principles that have made us what we are and have endeared our Party to the great heart of the people. In a word I stood unflinchingly on the plank of popular representation."

"And you?" said the Saint to her of the demi-monde.

"I wanted money," said the demi-mondaine.

And after some moments' thought the

Saint said: "Well, come in; though you don't deserve to."

But to the demagogue he said: "We genuinely regret that the limited space at our disposal and our unfortunate lack of interest in those Questions that you have gone so far to inculcate and have so ably upheld in the past, prevent us from giving you the support for which you seek."

And he shut the golden door.

THE GIANT POPPY

I DREAMT that I went back to the hills I knew, whence on a clear day you can see the walls of Ilion and the plains of Roncesvalles. There used to be woods along the tops of those hills with clearings in them where the moonlight fell, and there when no one watched the fairies danced.

But there were no woods when I went back, no fairies nor distant glimpse of Ilion or plains of Roncesvalles, only one giant poppy waved in the wind, and as it waved it hummed "Remember not." And by its oak-like stem a poet sat, dressed like a shepherd and playing an ancient tune softly upon a pipe. I asked him if the fairies had passed that way or anything olden.

He said: "The poppy has grown apace and is killing gods and fairies. Its fumes

51

are suffocating the world, and its roots drain it of its beautiful strength." And I asked him why he sat on the hills I knew, playing an olden tune.

And he answered: "Because the tune is bad for the poppy, which would otherwise grow more swiftly; and because if the brotherhood of which I am one were to cease to pipe on the hills men would stray over the world and be lost or come to terrible ends. We think we have saved Agamemnon."

Then he fell to piping again that olden tune, while the wind among the poppy's sleepy petals murmured "Remember not. Remember not."

ROSES

I KNOW a roadside where the wild rose blooms with a strange abundance. There is a beauty in the blossoms too of an almost exotic kind, a taint of deeper pink that shocks the Puritan flowers. Two hundred generations ago (generations, I mean, of roses) this was a village street; there was a floral decadence when they left their simple life and the roses came from the wilderness to clamber round houses of men.

Of all the memories of that little village, of all the cottages that stood there, of all the men and women whose homes they were, nothing remains but a more beautiful blush on the faces of the roses.

I hope that when London is clean passed away and the defeated fields come back

again, like an exiled people returning after
a war, they may find some beautiful thing
to remind them of it all; because we have
loved a little that swart old city.

THE MAN WITH THE GOLDEN EAR-RINGS

IT may be that I dreamed this. So much at least is certain—that I turned one day from the traffic of a city, and came to its docks and saw its slimy wharves going down green and steep into the water, and saw the huge grey river slipping by and the lost things that went with it turning over and over, and I thought of the nations and unpitying Time, and saw and marvelled at the queenly ships come newly from the sea.

It was then, if I mistake not, that I saw leaning against a wall, with his face to the ships, a man with golden ear-rings. His skin had the dark tint of the southern men: the deep black hairs of his moustache were whitened a little with salt; he wore a dark blue jacket such as sailors wear, and the long boots of seafarers, but the look in his eyes was further afield than the ships, he seemed to be beholding the farthest things.

Even when I spoke to him he did not call home that look, but answered me dreamily with that same fixed stare as though his thoughts were heaving on far and lonely seas. I asked him what ship he had come by, for there were many there. The sailing ships were there with their sails all furled and their masts straight and still like a wintry forest; the steamers were there, and great liners, puffing up idle smoke into the twilight. He answered he had come by none of them. I asked him what line he worked on, for he was clearly a sailor; I mentioned well-known lines, but he did not know them. Then I asked him where he worked and what he was. And he said: "I work in the Sargasso Sea, and I am the last of the pirates, the last left alive." And I shook him by the hand I do not know how many times. I said: "We feared you were dead. We feared you were dead." And he answered sadly: "No. No. I have sinned too deeply on the Spanish seas: I am not allowed to die."

THE DREAM OF KING KARNA-VOOTRA

KING KARNA-VOOTRA sitting on his throne commanding all things said: "I very clearly saw last night the queenly Vava-Nyria. Though partly she was hidden by great clouds that swept continually by her, rolling over and over, yet her face was unhidden and shone, being full of moonlight.

"I said to her: 'Walk with me by the great pools in many-gardened, beautiful Istrakhan where the lilies float that give delectable dreams; or, drawing aside the curtain of hanging orchids, pass with me thence from the pools by a secret path through the else impassable jungle that fills the only way between the mountains that shut in Istrakhan. They shut it in and look on it with joy

at morning and at evening when the pools
are strange with light, till in their gladness
sometimes there melts the deadly snow that
kills upon lonely heights the mountaineer.
They have valleys among them older than
the wrinkles in the moon.

" 'Come with me thence or linger with
me there and either we shall come to romantic lands which the men of the caravans only
speak of in song; or else we shall listlessly
walk in a land so lovely that even the butterflies that float about it when they see their
images flash in the sacred pools are terrified
by their beauty, and each night we shall hear
the myriad nightingales all in one chorus
sing the stars to death. Do this and I will
send heralds far from here with tidings of
thy beauty; and they shall run and come to
Séndara and men shall know it there who
herd brown sheep; and from Séndara the
rumor shall spread on, down either bank of

the holy river of Zoth, till the people that make wattles in the plains shall hear of it and sing; but the heralds shall go northward along the hills until they come to Sooma. And in that golden city they shall tell the kings, that sit in their lofty alabaster house, of thy strange and sudden smiles. And often in distant markets shall thy story be told by merchants out from Sooma as they sit telling careless tales to lure men to their wares.

" 'And the heralds passing thence shall come even to Ingra, to Ingra where they dance. And there they shall tell of thee, so that thy name long hence shall be sung in that joyous city. And there they shall borrow camels and pass over the sands and go by desert ways to distant Nirid to tell of thee to the lonely men in the mountain monasteries.

" 'Come with me even now for it is Spring.' "

"And as I said this she faintly yet perceptibly shook her head.   And it was only then I remembered my youth was gone, and she dead forty years."

THE STORM

THEY saw a little ship that was far at sea and that went by the name of the *Petite Espérance*. And because of its uncouth rig and its lonely air and the look that it had of coming from strangers' lands they said: "It is neither a ship to greet nor desire, nor yet to succor when in the hands of the sea."

And the sea rose up as is the wont of the sea and the little ship from afar was in his hands, and frailer than ever seemed its feeble masts with their sails of fantastic cut and their alien flags. And the sea made a great and very triumphing voice, as the sea doth. And then there arose a wave that was very strong, even the ninth-born son of the hurricane and the tide, and hid the little

ship and hid the whole of the far parts of
the sea. Thereat said those who stood on
the good dry land:

" 'Twas but a little worthless, alien ship
and it is sunk at sea, and it is good and
right that the storm have spoil." And they
turned and watched the course of the
merchantmen, laden with silver and appeas-
ing spice; year after year they cheered them
into port and praised their goods and their
familiar sails. And many years went by.

And at last with decks and bulwarks
covered with cloth of gold; with age-old par-
rots that had known the troubadours, singing illustrious songs and preening their
feathers of gold; with a hold full of emeralds and rubies; all silken with Indian loot;
furling as it came in its way-worn alien sails,
a galleon glided into port, shutting the sunlight from the merchantmen: and lo! it
loomed the equal of the cliffs.

"Who are you," they asked, "far-trav-
elled wonderful ship?"

And they said: "The *Petite Espérance.*"

"O," said the people on shore. "We thought you were sunk at sea."

"Sunk at sea?" sang the sailors. "We could not be sunk at sea—we had the gods on board."

A MISTAKEN IDENTITY

FAME as she walked at evening in a city saw the painted face of Notoriety flaunting beneath a gas-lamp, and many kneeled unto her in the dirt of the road.

"Who are you?" Fame said to her.

"I am Fame," said Notoriety.

Then Fame stole softly away so that no one knew she had gone.

And Notoriety presently went forth and all her worshippers rose and followed after, and she led them, as was most meet, to her native Pit.

THE TRUE HISTORY OF THE HARE AND THE TORTOISE

FOR a long time there was doubt with acrimony among the beasts as to whether the Hare or the Tortoise could run the swifter. Some said the Hare was the swifter of the two because he had such long ears, and others said that the Tortoise was the swifter because anyone whose shell was so hard as that should be able to run hard too. And lo, the forces of estrangement and disorder perpetually postponed a decisive contest.

But when there was nearly war among the beasts, at last an arrangement was come to and it was decided that the Hare and the Tortoise should run a race of five hundred yards so that all should see who was right.

"Ridiculous nonsense!" said the Hare,

and it was all his backers could do to get him to run.

"The contest is most welcome to me," said the Tortoise. "I shall not shirk it."

O, how his backers cheered.

Feeling ran high on the day of the race; the goose rushed at the fox and nearly pecked him. Both sides spoke loudly of the approaching victory up to the very moment of the race.

"I am absolutely confident of success," said the Tortoise. But the Hare said nothing, he looked bored and cross. Some of his supporters deserted him then and went to the other side, who were loudly cheering the Tortoise's inspiriting words. But many remained with the Hare. "We shall not be disappointed in him," they said. "A beast with such long ears is bound to win."

"Run hard," said the supporters of the Tortoise.

And "run hard" became a kind of catch-phrase which everybody repeated to one another. "Hard shell and hard living. That's what the country wants. Run hard," they said. And these words were never uttered but multitudes cheered from their hearts.

Then they were off, and suddenly there was a hush.

The Hare dashed off for about a hundred yards, then he looked round to see where his rival was.

"It is rather absurd," he said, "to race with a Tortoise." And he sat down and scratched himself. "Run hard! Run hard!" shouted some.

"Let him rest," shouted others. And "let him rest" became a catch-phrase too.

And after a while his rival drew near to him.

"There comes that damned Tortoise," said the Hare, and he got up and ran as hard as he could so that he should not let the Tortoise beat him.

"Those ears will win," said his friends. "Those ears will win; and establish upon

an incontestable footing the truth of what
we have said." And some of them turned
to the backers of the Tortoise and said:
"What about your beast now?"

"Run hard," they replied. "Run hard."

The Hare ran on for nearly three hundred
yards, nearly in fact as far as the winning-
post, when it suddenly struck him what a
fool he looked running races with a Tortoise who was nowhere in sight, and he
sat down again and scratched.

"Run hard. Run hard," said the crowd,
and "Let him rest."

"Whatever is the use of it?" said the
Hare, and this time he stopped for good.
Some say he slept.

There was desperate excitement for an
hour or two, and then the Tortoise won.

"Run hard. Run hard," shouted his backers. "Hard shell and hard living: that's
what has done it." And then they asked
the Tortoise what his achievement signified,
and he went and asked the Turtle. And

the Turtle said: "It is a glorious victory
for the forces of swiftness." And then
the Tortoise repeated it to his friends. And
all the beasts said nothing else for years.
And even to this day "a glorious victory for
the forces of swiftness" is a catch-phrase
in the house of the snail.

And the reason that this version of the
race is not widely known is that very few
of those that witnessed it survived the great
forest-fire that happened shortly after. It
came up over the weald by night with a
great wind. The Hare and the Tortoise
and a very few of the beasts saw it far off
from a high bare hill that was at the edge
of the trees, and they hurriedly called a meet-
ing to decide what messenger they should
send to warn the beasts in the forest.

They sent the Tortoise.

ALONE THE IMMORTALS

I HEARD it said that far away from here, on the wrong side of the deserts of Cathay and in a country dedicate to winter, are all the years that are dead. And there a certain valley shuts them in and hides them, as rumor has it, from the world, but not from the sight of the moon nor from those that dream in his rays.

And I said: I will go from here by ways of dream and I will come to that valley and enter in and mourn there for the good years that are dead. And I said: I will take a wreath, a wreath of mourning, and lay it at their feet in token of my sorrow for their dooms.

And when I sought about among the flowers, among the flowers for my wreath of mourning, the lily looked too large and the laurel looked too solemn and I found nothing frail enough nor slender to serve as an offering to the years that were dead. And at last I made a slender wreath of daisies in the manner that I had seen them made in one of the years that is dead.

"This," said I, "is scarce less fragile or less frail than one of those delicate forgotten years." Then I took my wreath in my hand and went from here. And when I had come by paths of mystery to that romantic land, where the valley that rumor told of lies close to the mountainous moon, I searched among the grass for those poor slight years for whom I brought my sorrow and my wreath. And when I found there nothing in the grass I said: "Time has shattered them and swept them away and left not even any faint remains."

But looking upwards in the blaze of the moon I suddenly saw colossi sitting near, and towering up and blotting out the stars and filling the night with blackness; and at those idols' feet I saw praying and making obeisance kings and the days that are and all times and all cities and all nations and all their gods. Neither the smoke of incense nor of the sacrifice burning reached those colossal heads, they sat there not to be measured, not to be overthrown, not to be worn away.

I said: "Who are those?"

One answered: "Alone the Immortals."

And I said sadly: "I came not to see dread gods, but I came to shed my tears and to offer flowers at the feet of certain little years that are dead and may not come again."

He answered me: "These *are* the years that are dead, alone the immortals; all years to be are Their children—They fashioned their smiles and their laughter; all earthly kings They have crowned, all gods They have created; all the events to be flow down from Their feet like a river, the worlds are flying pebbles that They have already thrown, and Time and all his centuries behind him kneel there with bended crests in token of vassalage at Their potent feet."

And when I heard this I turned away with my wreath, and went back to my own land comforted.

A MORAL LITTLE TALE

THERE was once an earnest Puritan who held it wrong to dance. And for his principles he labored hard, his was a zealous life. And there loved him all of those who hated the dance; and those that loved the dance respected him too; they said "He is a pure, good man and acts according to his lights."

He did much to discourage dancing and helped to close several Sunday entertainments. Some kinds of poetry, he said, he liked, but not the fanciful kind as that might corrupt the thoughts of the very young. He always dressed in black.

He was interested in morality and was quite sincere and there grew to be much respect on Earth for his honest face and his flowing pure-white beard.

One night the Devil appeared unto him in a dream and said "Well done."

"Avaunt," said that earnest man.

"No, no, friend," said the Devil.

"Dare not to call me 'friend,'" he answered bravely.

"Come, come, friend," said the Devil. "Have you not done my work? Have you not put apart the couples that would dance? Have you not checked their laughter and their accursed mirth? Have you not worn my livery of black? O friend, friend, you do not know what a detestable thing it is to sit in hell and hear people being happy, and singing in theatres and singing in the fields, and whispering after dances under the moon," and he fell to cursing fearfully.

"It is you," said the Puritan, "that put into their hearts the evil desire to dance; and black is God's own livery, not yours."

And the Devil laughed contemptuously and spoke.

"He only made the silly colors," he said,

"and useless dawns on hill-slopes facing South, and butterflies flapping along them as soon as the sun rose high, and foolish maidens coming out to dance, and the warm mad West wind, and worst of all that pernicious influence Love."

And when the Devil said that God made Love that earnest man sat up in bed and shouted "Blasphemy! Blasphemy!"

"It's true," said the Devil. "It isn't I that send the village fools muttering and whispering two by two in the woods when the harvest moon is high, it's as much as I can bear even to see them dancing."

"Then," said the man, "I have mistaken right for wrong; but as soon as I wake I will fight you yet."

"O, no you don't," said the Devil. "You don't wake up out of this sleep."

And somewhere far away Hell's black steel doors were opened, and arm in arm those two were drawn within, and the doors shut behind them and still they went arm in arm, trudging further and further into the deeps of Hell, and it was that Puritan's punishment to know that those that he cared for on Earth would do evil as he had done.

THE RETURN OF SONG

"THE swans are singing again," said to one another the gods. And looking downwards, for my dreams had taken me to some fair and far Valhalla, I saw below me an iridescent bubble not greatly larger than a star shine beautifully but faintly, and up and up from it looking larger and larger came a flock of white, innumerable swans, singing and singing and singing, till it seemed as though even the gods were wild ships swimming in music.

"What is it?" I said to one that was humble among the gods.

"Only a world has ended," he said to me, "and the swans are coming back to the gods returning the gift of song."

"A whole world dead!" I said.

"Dead," said he that was humble among

the gods. "The worlds are not for ever; only song is immortal."

"Look! Look!" he said. "There will be a new one soon."

And I looked and saw the larks, going down from the gods.

SPRING IN TOWN

A T a street corner sat, and played with a wind, Winter disconsolate.

Still tingled the fingers of the passers-by and still their breath was visible, and still they huddled their chins into their coats when turning a corner they met with a new wind, still windows lighted early sent out into the street the thought of romantic comfort by evening fires; these things still were, yet the throne of Winter tottered, and every breeze brought tidings of further fortresses lost on lakes or boreal hill-slopes. And not any longer as a king did Winter appear in those streets, as when the city was decked with gleaming white to greet him as a conqueror and he rode in with his glittering icicles and haughty retinue of prancing winds, but he sat there with a little wind at the corner of the street like some old blind beggar with his hungry dog. And as to some old blind beggar Death approaches, and the alert ears of the sightless man prophetically hear his far-off footfall, so there came suddenly to Winter's ears the sound, from some neighboring garden, of Spring approaching as she walked on daisies. And Spring approaching looked at huddled inglorious Winter.

"Begone," said Spring.

"There is nothing for you to do here," said Winter to her. Nevertheless he drew about him his grey and battered cloak and rose and called to his little bitter wind and up a side street that led northward strode away.

Pieces of paper and tall clouds of dust went with him as far as the city's outer gate. He turned then and called to Spring: "You can do nothing in this city," he said; then he marched homeward over plains and sea and heard his old winds howling as he marched. The ice broke up behind him and foundered like navies. To left and to right of him flew the flocks of the sea-birds, and far before him the geese's triumphant cry went like a clarion. Greater and greater grew his stature as he went northwards and ever more kingly his mien. Now he took baronies at a stride and now counties and came again to the snow-white frozen lands where the wolves came out to meet him and, draping himself anew with old grey clouds, strode through the gates of his invincible home, two old ice barriers swinging on pillars of ice that had never known the sun.

So the town was left to Spring. And she peered about to see what she could do with it. Presently she saw a dejected dog coming prowling down the road, so she sang to him and he gambolled. I saw him next day strutting by with something of an air. Where there were trees she went to them and whispered, and they sang the arboreal song that only trees can hear, and the green buds came peeping out as stars while yet it is twilight, secretly one by one. She went to gardens and awaked from dreaming the warm maternal earth. In little patches bare and desolate she called up like a flame the golden crocus, or its purple brother like an emperor's ghost. She gladdened the grace-less backs of untidy houses, here with a weed, there with a little grass. She said to the air, "Be joyous."

Children began to know that daisies blew in unfrequented corners. Buttonholes began to appear in the coats of the young men. The work of Spring was accomplished.

HOW THE ENEMY CAME TO THLŪNRĀNA

I T had been prophesied of old and fore-
seen from the ancient days that its enemy would come upon Thlūnrāna. And the
date of its doom was known and the gate
by which it would enter, yet none had
prophesied of the enemy who he was save
that he was of the gods though he dwelt
with men. Meanwhile Thlūnrāna, that secret lamaserai, that chief cathedral of wizardry, was the terror of the valley in which
it stood and of all lands round about it.
So narrow and high were the windows and
so strange when lighted at night that they
seemed to regard men with the demoniac
leer of something that had a secret in the
dark. Who were the magicians and the
deputy-magicians and the great arch-wizard

of that furtive place nobody knew, for they went veiled and hooded and cloaked completely in black.

Though her doom was close upon her and the enemy of prophecy should come that very night through the open, southward door that was named the Gate of the Doom, yet that rocky edifice Thlūnrāna remained mysterious still, venerable, terrible, dark, and dreadfully crowned with her doom. It was not often that anyone dared wander near to Thlūnrāna by night when the moan of the magicians invoking we know not Whom rose faintly from inner chambers, scaring the drifting bats: but on the last night of all the man from the black-thatched cottage by the five pine-trees came, because he would see Thlūnrāna once again before the enemy that was divine, but that dwelt with man, should come against it and it should be no more. Up the dark valley he went like a bold man, but his fears were thick upon him; his bravery bore their weight but stooped a little beneath them. He went in at the southward gate that is named the Gate of the Doom. He came into a dark hall, and up a marble stairway passed to see the last of Thlūnrāna. At the top a curtain of black velvet hung and he passed into a chamber heavily hung with curtains, with a gloom in it that was blacker than anything they could account for. In a sombre chamber beyond, seen through a vacant archway, magicians with lighted tapers plied their wizardry and whispered incantations. All the rats in the place were passing away, going whimpering down the stairway. The man from the black-thatched cottage passed through that second chamber: the magicians did not look at him and did not cease to whisper. He passed from them through heavy curtains still of black velvet and came into a chamber of black marble where nothing stirred. Only one taper burned in the third chamber; there were no windows. On the smooth floor and under the smooth wall a silk pavilion stood with its curtains drawn close together: this was the holy of holies of that ominous place, its inner mystery. One on each side of it dark figures crouched, either of men or women or cloaked stone, or of beasts trained to be silent. When the awful stillness of the mystery was more than he could bear the man from the black-thatched cottage by the five pine-trees went up to the silk pavilion, and with a bold and nervous clutch of the hand drew one of the curtains aside, and saw the inner mystery, and laughed. And the prophecy was fulfilled, and Thlūnrāna was never more a terror to the valley, but the magicians passed away from their terrific halls and fled through the open fields wailing and beating their breasts, for laughter was the enemy that was doomed to come against Thlūnrāna through her southward gate (that was named the Gate of the Doom), and it is of the gods but dwells with man.

A LOSING GAME

ONCE in a tavern Man met face to skull with Death. Man entered gaily but Death gave no greeting, he sat with his jowl morosely over an ominous wine.

"Come, come," said Man, "we have been antagonists long, and if I were losing yet I should not be surly."

But Death remained unfriendly watching his bowl of wine and gave no word in answer.

Then Man solicitously moved nearer to him and, speaking cheerily still, "Come, come," he said again, "you must not resent defeat."

And still Death was gloomy and cross and sipped at his infamous wine and would not look up at Man and would not be companionable.

89

But Man hated gloom either in beast or god, and it made him unhappy to see his adversary's discomfort, all the more because he was the cause, and still he tried to cheer him.

"Have you not slain the Dinatherium?" he said. "Have you not put out the Moon? Why! you will beat me yet."

And with a dry and barking sound Death wept and nothing said; and presently Man arose and went wondering away; for he knew not if Death wept out of pity for his opponent, or because he knew that he should not have such sport again when the old game was over and Man was gone, or whether because perhaps, for some hidden reason, he could never repeat on Earth his triumph over the Moon.

TAKING UP PICCADILLY

GOING down Piccadilly one day and nearing Grosvenor Place I saw, if my memory is not at fault, some workmen with their coats off—or so they seemed. They had pickaxes in their hands and wore corduroy trousers and that little leather band below the knee that goes by the astonishing name of "York-to-London."

They seemed to be working with peculiar vehemence, so that I stopped and asked one what they were doing.

"We are taking up Piccadilly," he said to me.

"But at this time of year?" I said. "Is it usual in June?"

"We are not what we seem," said he.

"Oh, I see," I said, "you are doing it for a joke."

"Well not exactly that," he answered me.

"For a bet?" I said.

"Not precisely," said he.

And then I looked at the bit that they had already picked, and though it was broad daylight over my head it was darkness down there, all full of the southern stars.

"It was noisy and bad and we grew aweary of it," said he that wore corduroy trousers. "We are not what we appear."

They were taking up Piccadilly altogether.

AFTER THE FIRE

WHEN that happened which had been so long in happening and the world hit a black, uncharted star, certain tremendous creatures out of some other world came peering among the cinders to see if there were anything there that it were worth while to remember. They spoke of the great things that the world was known to have had; they mentioned the mammoth. And presently they saw man's temples, silent and windowless, staring like empty skulls.

"Some great thing has been here," one said, "in these huge places." "It was the mammoth," said one. "Something greater than he," said another.

And then they found that the greatest thing in the world had been the dreams of man.

THE CITY

IN time as well as in space my fancy roams far from here. It led me once to the edge of certain cliffs that were low and red and rose up out of a desert: a little way off in the desert there was a city. It was evening, and I sat and watched the city.

Presently I saw men by threes and fours come softly stealing out of that city's gate to the number of about twenty. I heard the hum of men's voices speaking at evening.

"It is well they are gone," they said. "It is well they are gone. We can do business now. It is well they are gone." And the men that had left the city sped away over the sand and so passed into the twilight.

"Who are these men?" I said to my glittering leader.

"The poets," my fancy answered. "The poets and artists."

94

"Why do they steal away?" I said to him. "And why are the people glad that they have gone?"

He said: "It must be some doom that is going to fall on the city, something has warned them and they have stolen away. Nothing may warn the people."

I heard the wrangling voices, glad with commerce, rise up from the city. And then I also departed, for there was an ominous look on the face of the sky.

And only a thousand years later I passed that way, and there was nothing, even among the weeds, of what had been that city.

THE FOOD OF DEATH

DEATH was sick. But they brought him bread that the modern bakers make, whitened with alum, and the tinned meats of Chicago, with a pinch of our modern substitute for salt. They carried him into the dining-room of a great hotel (in that close atmosphere Death breathed more freely), and there they gave him their cheap Indian tea. They brought him a bottle of wine that they called champagne. Death drank it up. They bought a newspaper and looked up the patent medicines; they gave him the foods that it recommended for invalids, and a little medicine as prescribed in the paper. They gave him some milk and borax, such as children drink in England.

Death arose ravening, strong, and strode again through the cities.

THE LONELY IDOL

I HAD from a friend an old outlandish stone, a little swine-faced idol to whom no one prayed.

And when I saw his melancholy case as he sat cross-legged at receipt of prayer, holding a little scourge that the years had broken (and no one heeded the scourge and no one prayed and no one came with squealing sacrifice; and he had been a god), then I took pity on the little forgotten thing and prayed to it as perhaps they prayed long since, before the coming of the strange dark ships, and humbled myself and said:

"O idol, idol of the hard pale stone, invincible to the years, O scourge-holder, give ear for behold I pray.

"O little pale-green image whose wanderings are from far, know thou that here in

Europe and in other lands near by, too soon there pass from us the sweets and song and the lion strength of youth: too soon do their cheeks fade, their hair grow grey and our beloved die; too brittle is beauty, too far off is fame and the years are gathered too soon; there are leaves, leaves falling, everywhere falling; there is autumn among men, autumn and reaping; failure there is, struggle, dying and weeping, and all that is beautiful hath not remained but is even as the glory of morning upon the water.

"Even our memories are gathered too with the sound of the ancient voices, the pleasant ancient voices that come to our ears no more; the very gardens of our childhood fade, and there dims with the speed of the years even the mind's own eye.

"O be not any more the friend of Time, for the silent hurry of his malevolent feet have trodden down what's fairest; I almost hear the whimper of the years running behind him hound-like, and it takes few to tear us.

"All that is beautiful he crushes down as a big man tramples daisies, all that is fairest. How very fair are the little children of men. It is autumn with all the world, and the stars weep to see it.

"Therefore no longer be the friend of Time, who will not let us be, and be not good to him but pity us, and let lovely things live on for the sake of our tears."

Thus prayed I out of compassion one windy day to the snout-faced idol to whom no one kneeled.

THE SPHINX IN THEBES
(MASSACHUSETTS)

THERE was a woman in a steel-built city who had all that money could buy, she had gold and dividends and trains and houses, and she had pets to play with, but she had no sphinx.

So she besought them to bring her a live sphinx; and therefore they went to the menageries, and then to the forests and the desert places, and yet could find no sphinx.

And she would have been content with a little lion but that one was already owned by a woman she knew; so they had to search the world again for a sphinx.

And still there was none.

But they were not men that it is easy to baffle, and at last they found a sphinx in a desert at evening watching a ruined temple whose gods she had eaten hundreds of years ago when her hunger was on her. And they cast chains on her, who was still with an ominous stillness, and took her westwards with them and brought her home.

And so the sphinx came to the steel-built city.

And the woman was very glad that she owned a sphinx: but the sphinx stared long into her eyes one day, and softly asked a riddle of the woman.

And the woman could not answer, and she died.

And the sphinx is silent again and none knows what she will do.

THE REWARD

ONE'S spirit goes further in dreams than it does by day. Wandering once by night from a factory city I came to the edge of Hell.

The place was foul with cinders and cast-off things, and jagged, half-buried things with shapeless edges, and there was a huge angel with a hammer building in plaster and steel. I wondered what he did in that dreadful place. I hesitated, then asked him what he was building. "We are adding to Hell," he said, "to keep pace with the times." "Don't be too hard on them," I said, for I had just come out of a compromising age and a weakening country. The angel did not answer. "It won't be as bad as the old hell, will it?" I said. "Worse," said the angel.

"How can you reconcile it with your conscience as a Minister of Grace," I said, "to inflict such a punishment?" (They talked like this in the city whence I had come and I could not avoid the habit of it.)

"They have invented a new cheap yeast," said the angel.

I looked at the legend on the walls of the hell that the angel was building, the words were written in flame, every fifteen seconds they changed their color, "Yeasto, the great new yeast, it builds up body and brain, and something more."

"They shall look at it for ever," the angel said.

"But they drove a perfectly legitimate trade," I said, "the law allowed it."

The angel went on hammering into place the huge steel uprights.

"You are very revengeful," I said. "Do you never rest from doing this terrible work?"

"I rested one Christmas Day," the angel

said, "and looked and saw little children dying of cancer. I shall go on now until the fires are lit."

"It is very hard to prove," I said, "that the yeast is as bad as you think."

"After all," I said, "they must live."

And the angel made no answer but went on building his hell.

THE TROUBLE IN LEAFY
GREEN STREET

SHE went to the idol-shop in Moleshill
Street, where the old man mumbles,
and said: "I want a god to worship when it
is wet."

The old man reminded her of the heavy
penalties that rightly attach to idolatry and,
when he had enumerated all, she answered
him as was meet: "Give me a god to worship when it is wet."

And he went to the back places of his
shop and sought out and brought her a god.
The same was carved of grey stone and wore
a propitious look and was named, as the old
man mumbled, The God of Rainy Cheerfulness.

Now it may be that long confinement to
the house affects adversely the liver, or

these things may be of the soul, but certain it is that on a rainy day her spirits so far descended that those cheerful creatures came within sight of the Pit, and, having tried cigarettes to no good end, she bethought her of Moleshill Street and the mumbling man.

He brought the grey idol forth and mumbled of guarantees, although he put nothing on paper, and she paid him there and then his preposterous price and took the idol away.

And on the next wet day that there ever was she prayed to the grey-stone idol that she had bought, the God of Rainy Cheerfulness (who knows with what ceremony or what lack of it?), and so brought down on her in Leafy Green Street, in the prosperous house at the corner, that doom of which all men speak.

THE MIST

THE mist said unto the mist: "Let us go up into the Downs." And the mist came up weeping.

And the mist went into the high places and the hollows.

And clumps of trees in the distance stood ghostly in the haze.

But I went to a prophet, one who loved the Downs, and I said to him: "Why does the mist come up weeping into the Downs when it goes into the high places and the hollows?"

And he answered: "The mist is the company of a multitude of souls who never saw the Downs, and now are dead. Therefore they come up weeping into the Downs, who are dead and never saw them."

FURROW-MAKER

HE was all in black, but his friend was dressed in brown, members of two old families.

"Is there any change in the way you build your houses?" said he in black.

"No change," said the other. "And you?"

"We change not," he said.

A man went by in the distance riding a bicycle.

"He is always changing," said the one in black, "of late almost every century. He is uneasy. Always changing."

"He changes the way he builds his house, does he not?" said the brown one.

"So my family say," said the other. "They say he has changed of late."

"They say he takes much to cities?" the brown one said.

"My cousin who lives in belfries tells me so," said the black one. "He says he is much in cities."

"And there he grows lean?" said the brown one.

"Yes, he grows lean."

"Is it true what they say?" said the brown one.

"Caw," said the black one.

"Is it true that he cannot live many centuries?"

"No, no," said the black one. "Furrow-maker will not die. We must not lose furrow-maker. He has been foolish of late, he has played with smoke and is sick. His engines have wearied him and his cities are evil. Yes, he is very sick. But in a few centuries he will forget his folly and we shall not lose furrow-maker. Time out of mind he has delved and my family have got their food from the raw earth behind him. He will not die."

"But they say, do they not?" said the

brown one, "his cities are noisome, and that he grows sick in them and can run no longer, and that it is with him as it is with us when we grow too many, and the grass has the bitter taste in the rainy season, and our young grow bloated and die."

"Who says it?" replied the black one.

"Pigeon," the brown one answered. "He came back all dirty. And Hare went down to the edge of the cities once. He says it too. Man was too sick to chase him. He thinks that Man will die, and his wicked friend Dog with him. Dog, he will die. That nasty fellow Dog. He will die too, the dirty fellow!"

"Pigeon and Hare!" said the black one. "We shall not lose furrow-maker."

"Who told you he will not die?" his brown friend said.

"Who told me!" the black one said. "My family and his have understood each other times out of mind. We know what follies will kill each other and what each may survive, and I say that furrow-maker will not die."

"He will die," said the brown one.

"Caw," said the other.

And Man said in his heart: "Just one invention more. There is something I want to do with petrol yet, and then I will give it all up and go back to the woods."

LOBSTER SALAD

I WAS climbing round the perilous outside of the Palace of Colquonhombros. So far below me that in the tranquil twilight and clear air of those lands I could only barely see them lay the craggy tops of the mountains.

It was along no battlements or terrace edge I was climbing, but on the sheer face of the wall itself, getting what foothold I could where the boulders joined.

Had my feet been bare I was done, but though I was in my night-shirt I had on stout leather boots, and their edges somehow held in those narrow cracks. My fingers and wrists were aching.

Had it been possible to stop for a moment I might have been lured to give a second look at the fearful peaks of the mountains down there in the twilight, and this must have been fatal.

That the thing was all a dream is beside the point. We have fallen in dreams before, but it is well known that if in one of those falls you ever hit the ground—you die: I had looked at those menacing mountain-tops and knew well that such a fall as the one I feared must have such a termination. Then I went on.

It is strange what different sensations there can be in different boulders—every one gleaming with the same white light and every one chosen to match the rest by minions of ancient kings—when your life depends on the edges of every one you come to. Those edges seemed strangely different. It was of no avail to overcome the terror of one, for the next would give you a hold in quite a different way or hand you over to death in a different manner. Some were too sharp to hold and some too flush with the wall, those whose hold was the best crumbled the soonest; each rock had its different terror: and then there were those things that followed behind me.

And at last I came to a breach made long ago by earthquake, lightning or war: I should have had to go down a thousand feet to get round it and they would come up with me while I was doing that, for certain sable apes that I have not mentioned as yet, things that had tigerish teeth and were born and bred on that wall, had pursued me all the evening. In any case I could have gone no farther, nor did I know what the king would do along whose wall I was climbing. It was time to drop and be done with it or stop and await those apes.

And then it was that I remembered a pin, thrown carelessly down out of an evening-tie in another world to the one where grew that glittering wall, and lying now if no evil chance had removed it on a chest of drawers by my bed. The apes were very close, and hurrying, for they knew my fingers were slipping, and the cruel peaks of those infernal mountains seemed surer of me than the apes. I reached out with a desperate effort of will towards where the pin lay on the chest of drawers. I groped about. I found it! I ran it into my arm. Saved!

THE RETURN OF THE EXILES

THE old man with a hammer and the one-eyed man with a spear were seated by the roadside talking as I came up the hill.

"It isn't as though they hadn't asked us," the one with the hammer said.

"There ain't no more than twenty as knows about it," said the other.

"Twenty's twenty," said the first.

"After all these years," said the one-eyed man with the spear. "After all these years. We might go back just once."

"O' course we might," said the other.

Their clothes were old even for laborers, the one with the hammer had a leather apron full of holes and blackened, and their hands looked like leather. But whatever they were they were English, and this was

116

pleasant to see after all the motors that had passed me that day with their burden of mixed and doubtful nationalities.

When they saw me the one with the hammer touched his greasy cap.

"Might we make so bold, sir," he said, "as to ask the way to Stonehenge?"

"We never ought to go," mumbled the other plaintively. "There's not more than twenty as knows, but . . ."

I was bicycling there myself to see the place so I pointed out the way and rode on at once, for there was something so utterly servile about them both that I did not care for their company. They seemed by their wretched mien to have been persecuted or utterly neglected for many years, I thought that very likely they had done long terms of penal servitude.

When I came to Stonehenge I saw a group of about a score of men standing among the stones. They asked me with some solemnity if I was expecting anyone, and when I said No they spoke to me no more. It was three miles back where I left those strange old men, but I had not been in the stone circle long when they appeared, coming with great strides along the road. When they saw them all the people took off their hats and acted very strangely, and I saw that they had a goat which they led up then to the old altar stone. And the two old men came up with their hammer and spear and began apologizing plaintively for the liberty they had taken in coming back to that place, and all the people knelt on the grass before them. And then still kneeling they killed the goat by the altar, and when the two old men saw this they came up with many excuses and eagerly sniffed the blood. And at first this made them happy. But soon the one with the spear began to whimper. "It used to be men," he lamented. "It used to be men."

And the twenty men began looking uneasily at each other, and the plaint of the one-eyed man went on in that tearful voice, and all of a sudden they all looked at me. I do not know who the two old men were or what any of them were doing, but there are moments when it is clearly time to go, and I left them there and then. And just as I got up on to my bicycle I heard the plaintive voice of the one with the hammer apologizing for the liberty he had taken in coming back to Stonehenge.

"But after all these years," I heard him crying, "After all these years. . . ."

And the one with the spear said: "Yes, after three thousand years. . . ."

NATURE AND TIME

THROUGH the streets of Coventry one winter's night strode a triumphant spirit. Behind him stooping, unkempt, utterly ragged, wearing the clothes and look that outcasts have, whining, weeping, reproaching, an ill-used spirit tried to keep pace with him. Continually she plucked him by the sleeve and cried out to him as she panted after and he strode resolute on.

It was a bitter night, yet it did not seem to be the cold that she feared, ill-clad though she was, but the trams and the ugly shops and the glare of the factories, from which she continually winced as she hobbled on, and the pavement hurt her feet.

He that strode on in front seemed to care for nothing, it might be hot or cold, silent or noisy, pavement or open fields, he merely had the air of striding on.

And she caught up and clutched him by the elbow. I heard her speak in her unhappy voice, you scarcely heard it for the noise of the traffic.

"You have forgotten me," she complained to him. "You have forsaken me here."

She pointed to Coventry with a wide wave of her arm and seemed to indicate other cities beyond. And he gruffly told her to keep pace with him and that he did not forsake her. And she went on with her pitiful lamentation.

"My anemones are dead for miles," she said, "all my woods are fallen and still the cities grow. My child Man is unhappy and my other children are dying, and still the cities grow and you have forgotten me!"

And then he turned angrily on her, almost stopping in that stride of his that began when the stars were made.

"When have I ever forgotten you?" he

said, "or when forsaken you ever? Did I not throw down Babylon for you? And is not Nineveh gone? Where is Persepolis that troubled you? Where Tarshish and Tyre? And you have said I forget you."

And at this she seemed to take a little comfort. I heard her speak once more, looking wistfully at her companion. "When will the fields come back and the grass for my children?"

"Soon, soon," he said: then they were silent. And he strode away, she limping along behind him, and all the clocks in the towers chimed as he passed.

THE SONG OF THE BLACKBIRD

A S the poet passed the thorn-tree the blackbird sang.

"How ever do you do it?" the poet said, for he knew bird language.

"It was like this," said the blackbird. "It really was the most extraordinary thing. I made that song last Spring, it came to me all of a sudden. There was the most beautiful she-blackbird that the world has ever seen. Her eyes were blacker than lakes are at night, her feathers were blacker than the night itself, and nothing was as yellow as her beak; she could fly much faster than the lightning. She was not an ordinary she-blackbird, there has never been any other like her at all. I did not dare go near her because she was so wonderful. One day last Spring when it got warm again—it had been cold, we ate berries, things were quite different then, but Spring came and it got warm —one day I was thinking how wonderful she was and it seemed so extraordinary to think that I should ever have seen her, the only really wonderful she-blackbird in the world, that I opened my beak to give a shout, and then this song came, and there had never been anything like it before, and luckily I remembered it, the very song that I just sang now. But what is so extraordinary, the most amazing occurrence of that marvellous day, was that no sooner had I sung the song than that very bird, the most wonderful she-blackbird in the world, flew right up to me and sat quite close to me on the same tree. I never remember such wonderful times as those.

"Yes, the song came in a moment, and as I was saying . . ."

And an old wanderer walking with a stick came by and the blackbird flew away, and the poet told the old man the blackbird's wonderful story.

"That song new?" said the wanderer. "Not a bit of it. God made it years ago. All the blackbirds used to sing it when I was young. It was new then."

THE MESSENGERS

ONE wandering nigh Parnassus chasing hares heard the high Muses.

"Take us a message to the Golden Town."
Thus sang the Muses.

But the man said: "They do not call to me. Not to such as me speak the Muses."

And the Muses called him by name.

"Take us a message," they said, "to the Golden Town."

And the man was downcast for he would have chased hares.

And the Muses called again.

And when whether in valleys or on high crags of the hills he still heard the Muses he went at last to them and heard their message, though he would fain have left it to other men and chased the fleet hares still in happy valleys.

And they gave him a wreath of laurels carved out of emeralds as only the Muses can carve. "By this," they said, "they shall know that you come from the Muses."

And the man went from that place and dressed in scarlet silks as befitted one that came from the high Muses. And through the gateway of the Golden Town he ran and cried his message, and his cloak floated behind him. All silent sat the wise men and the aged, they of the Golden Town; cross-legged they sat before their houses reading from parchments a message of the Muses that they sent long before.

And the young man cried his message from the Muses.

And they rose up and said: "Thou art not from the Muses. Otherwise spake they." And they stoned him and he died.

And afterwards they carved his message upon gold; and read it in their temples on holy days.

When will the Muses rest? When are

they weary? They sent another messenger to the Golden Town. And they gave him a wand of ivory to carry in his hand with all the beautiful stories of the world wondrously carved thereon. And only the Muses could have carved it. "By this," they said, "they shall know that you come from the Muses."

And he came through the gateway of the Golden Town with the message he had for its people. And they rose up at once in the Golden street, they rose from reading the message that they had carved upon gold. "The last who came," they said, "came with a wreath of laurels carved out of emeralds, as only the Muses can carve. You are not from the Muses."

And even as they had stoned the last so also they stoned him. And afterwards they carved his message on gold and laid it up in their temples.

When will the Muses rest? When are they weary? Even yet once again they sent a messenger under the gateway into the Golden Town. And for all that he wore a garland of gold that the high Muses gave him, a garland of kingcups soft and yellow on his head, yet fashioned of pure gold and by whom but the Muses, yet did they stone him in the Golden Town. But they had the message, and what care the Muses?

And yet they will not rest, for some while since I heard them call to me.

"Go take our message," they said, "unto the Golden Town."

But I would not go. And they spake a second time. "Go take our message," they said.

And still I would not go, and they cried out a third time: "Go take our message."

And though they cried a third time I would not go. But morning and night they cried and through long evenings.

When will the Muses rest? When are they weary? And when they would not cease to call to me I went to them and I said: "The Golden Town is the Golden Town no longer. They have sold their pillars for brass and their temples for money, they have made coins out of their golden doors. It is become a dark town full of trouble, there is no ease in its streets, beauty has left it and the old songs are gone."

"Go take our message," they cried.

And I said to the high Muses: "You do not understand. You have no message for the Golden Town, the holy city no longer."

"Go take our message," they cried.

"What is your message?" I said to the high Muses.

And when I heard their message I made excuses, dreading to speak such things in the Golden Town; and again they bade me go.

And I said: "I will not go. None will believe me."

And still the Muses cry to me all night long.

They do not understand. How should they know?

THE THREE TALL SONS

A ND at last Man raised on high the final glory of his civilization, the towering edifice of the ultimate city.

Softly beneath him in the deeps of the earth purred his machinery fulfilling all his needs, there was no more toil for man. There he sat at ease discussing the Sex Problem.

And sometimes painfully out of forgotten fields, there came to his outer door, came to the furthest rampart of the final glory of Man, a poor old woman begging. And always they turned her away. This glory of Man's achievement, this city was not for her.

It was Nature that thus came begging in from the fields, whom they always turned away.

And away she went again alone to her fields.

And one day she came again, and again they sent her hence. But her three tall sons came too.

"These shall go in," she said. "Even these my sons to your city."

And the three tall sons went in.

And these are Nature's sons, the forlorn one's terrible children, War, Famine and Plague.

Yea and they went in there and found Man unawares in his city still poring over his Problems, obsessed with his civilization, and never hearing their tread as those three came up behind.

COMPROMISE

THEY built their gorgeous home, their city of glory, above the lair of the earthquake. They built it of marble and gold in the shining youth of the world. There they feasted and fought and called their city immortal, and danced and sang songs to the gods. None heeded the earthquake in all those joyous streets. And down in the deeps of the earth, on the black feet of the abyss, they that would conquer Man mumbled long in the darkness, mumbled and goaded the earthquake to try his strength with that city, to go forth blithely at night and to gnaw its pillars like bones. And down in those grimy deeps the earthquake answered them, and would not do their pleasure and would not stir from thence, for who knew who they were who danced all day where he rumbled, and what

134

if the lords of that city that had no fear of his anger were haply even the gods!

And the centuries plodded by, on and on round the world, and one day they that had danced, they that had sung in that city, remembered the lair of the earthquake in the deeps down under their feet, and made plans one with another and sought to avert the danger, sought to appease the earthquake and turn his anger away.

They sent down singing girls, and priests with oats and wine, they sent down garlands and propitious berries, down by dark steps to the black depths of the earth, they sent peacocks newly slain, and boys with burning spices, and their thin white sacred cats with collars of pearls all newly drawn from sea, they sent huge diamonds down in coffers of teak, and ointment and strange oriental dyes, arrows and armor and the rings of their queen.

"Oho," said the earthquake in the coolth of the earth, "so they are not the gods."

WHAT WE HAVE COME TO

WHEN the advertiser saw the cathedral spires over the downs in the distance, he looked at them and wept.

"If only," he said, "this were an advertisement of Beefo, so nice, so nutritious, try it in your soup, ladies like it."

THE TOMB OF PAN

SEEING," they said, "that old-time Pan is dead, let us now make a tomb for him and a monument, that the dreadful worship of long ago may be remembered and avoided by all."

So said the people of the enlightened lands. And they built a white and mighty tomb of marble. Slowly it rose under the hands of the builders and longer every evening after sunset it gleaned with rays of the departed sun.

And many mourned for Pan while the builders built; many reviled him. Some called the builders to cease and to weep for Pan and others called them to leave no memorial at all of so infamous a god. But the builders built on steadily.

And one day all was finished, and the

tomb stood there like a steep sea-cliff. And Pan was carved thereon with humbled head and the feet of angels pressed upon his neck. And when the tomb was finished the sun had already set, but the afterglow was rosy on the huge bulk of Pan.

And presently all the enlightened people came, and saw the tomb and remembered Pan who was dead, and all deplored him and his wicked age. But a few wept apart because of the death of Pan.

But at evening as he stole out of the forest, and slipped like a shadow softly along the hills, Pan saw the tomb and laughed.

....other best selling
NEWCASTLE books

The Newcastle Forgotten Fantasy Library

GLITTERING PLAIN by William Morris $2.45

ERIC BRIGHT EYES by H. Rider Haggard $2.95

FOOD OF DEATH: FIFTY ONE TALES by Lord Dunsany $2.45

Self-Enrichment Books

MARRIAGE COUNSELING: FACT OR FALLACY? by Jerold R. Kuhn PhD. $2.95

NATURAL WAY TO HEALTH by Victor H. Lindlahr $2.95

EAT AND REDUCE by Victor H. Lindlahr $2.45

VITAMIN COOKBOOK by Victor H. Lindlahr $2.95

YOU ARE WHAT YOU EAT by Victor H. Lindlahr $2.25

VIEWPOINT ON NUTRITION by Dr. Arnold Pike $2.95

LOVE, HATE, FEAR, ANGER AND THE OTHER LIVELY EMOTIONS by June Callwood $2.45

FORTUNATE STRANGERS by Cornelius Beukenkamp Jr. M.D. $2.95

IMPORTANCE OF FEELING INFERIOR by Marie B. Ray $2.95

CONQUEST OF FEAR by Basil King $2.95

ROMANY REMEDIES AND RECIPES by Gipsy Petulengro $2.25

THOUGHT VIBRATIONS by A. Victor Segno $2.45

Occult Books

ARCANA OF ASTROLOGY by William J. Simmonite $3.95

KABALA OF NUMBERS by Sepharial $3.95

QUEST OF THE GOLDEN STAIRS by Arthur Edward Waite $2.95

BOOK OF DREAMS AND GHOSTS by Andrew Lang $2.95

DEVIL IN BRITAIN AND AMERICA by John Ashton $3.75

FORTUNE TELLING FOR FUN by Paul Showers $2.95

GHOSTS I HAVE MET by John Kendrick Bangs $2.45

GRAPHOANALYSIS: by William Leslie French $2.95

INTRODUCTION TO ASTROLOGY by William Lilly $3.75

LOST ATLANTIS by James Bramwell $3.45

MAGIC, WHITE AND BLACK by Franz Hartmann M.D. $3.45

NUMEROLOGY MADE PLAIN by Ariel Yvon Taylor $2.45

ORIGINS OF POPULAR SUPERSTITIONS AND CUSTOMS by T. Sharper Knowlson $2.95

PRACTICAL ASTROLOGY by Compte de Saint-Germain $2.95

PRACTICE OF PALMISTRY by Compte de Saint-Germain $3.95

RITUAL MAGIC by E. M. Butler $3.45

THIRTY YEARS AMONG THE DEAD by Carl A. Wickland, M.D. $3.95

Please check with your favorite Bookseller for any of the Books listed on this page or order directly from:

NEWCASTLE PUBLISHING COMPANY, INC.

1521 No. Vine St. Hollywood, California 90028

NOW *from*

NEWCASTLE

These 4 Bestselling Books

YOU ARE WHAT YOU EAT
$2.25

EAT AND REDUCE
$2.45

VITAMIN COOKBOOK
$2.95

THE NATURAL WAY TO HEALTH
$2.95

by Victor Lindlahr

VIEWPOINT ON NUTRITION by Dr. Arnold Pike is a practical guide to proper nutrition and keeping fit. This fine book features interviews with Gaylord Hauser, Eddie Albert, Julie Harris, Sugar Ray Robinson, Dr. Linus Pauling, Marty Allen and many others. You will learn how to select exactly the right diet for you. Also contains the complete government report – Human Nutrition No. 2 by the U.S. Department of Agriculture. Introduction by Gaylord Hauser. Includes photographs of many celebrities who have appeared on Dr. Pike's nationally syndicated show. A Newcastle original! Dr. Arnold Pike has been called America's Mr. Media of Nutrition. He is the host of the coast to coast award-winning radio and TV Series 'Viewpoint on Nutrition.'

232 Pages   5½ x 8½ $2.95

Please check with your favorite Bookseller for any of the books listed on this page or order directly from:

NEWCASTLE PUBLISHING COMPANY, INC.
1521 North Vine St., Hollywood California 90028